DAW...

THE POCKET
WATCHMAKER

PENGUIN BOOKS

PENGUIN BOOKS

Published by the Penguin Group. Penguin Books Ltd, 27 Wrights Lane, London w8 5tz, England. Penguin Books USA Inc., 375 Hudson Street, New York, New York 10014, USA. Penguin Books Australia Ltd, Ringwood, Victoria, Australia. Penguin Books Canada Ltd, 10 Alcorn Avenue, Toronto, Ontario, Canada M4V 3B2. Penguin Books (NZ) Ltd, 182 – 190 Wairau Road, Auckland 10, New Zealand · Penguin Books Ltd, Registered Offices: Harmondsworth, Middlesex, England · This extract is from *The Blind Watchmaker*, by Richard Dawkins, first published by Longman 1986. Published in Penguin Books 1988. This edition published 1996 · Copyright © Richard Dawkins, 1986. All rights reserved · Typeset by Rowland Phototypesetting Ltd, Bury St Edmunds, Suffolk. Printed in England by Clays Ltd, St Ives plc ·

I

We animals are the most complicated things in the known universe. The universe that we know is a tiny fragment of the actual universe. There may be yet more complicated objects than us on other planets, and some of them may already know about us. But this doesn't alter the point that I want to make. Complicated things, everywhere, deserve a very special kind of explanation. We want to know how they came into existence and why they are so complicated. The explanation, as I shall argue, is likely to be broadly the same for complicated things everywhere in the universe; the same for us, for chimpanzees, worms, oak trees and monsters from outer space. On the other hand, it will not be the same for what I shall call 'simple' things, such as rocks, clouds, rivers, galaxies and quarks. These are the stuff of physics. Chimps and dogs and bats and cockroaches and people and worms and dandelions and bacteria and galactic aliens are the stuff of biology.

The difference is one of complexity of design.

Biology is the study of complicated things that give the appearance of having been designed for a purpose. Physics is the study of simple things that do not tempt us to invoke design. At first sight, man-made artefacts like computers and cars will seem to provide exceptions. They are complicated and obviously designed for a purpose, yet they are not alive, and they are made of metal and plastic rather than of flesh and blood. In this book they will be firmly treated as biological objects.

The reader's reaction to this may be to ask, 'Yes, but are they *really* biological objects?' Words are our servants, not our masters. For different purposes we find it convenient to use words in different senses. Most cookery books class lobsters as fish. Zoologists can become quite apoplectic about this, pointing out that lobsters could with greater justice call humans fish, since fish are far closer kin to humans than they are to lobsters. Cooks and lawyers need to use words in their own special ways, and so do I in this book. Never mind whether cars and computers are 'really' biological objects. The point is that if anything of that degree of complexity were found on a planet, we should have no hesitation in concluding that life existed, or had once existed, on that planet. Machines are the direct products of living objects; they derive their complexity and design from living objects, and they are diagnostic of the existence of life on a planet. The same goes for fossils, skeletons and dead bodies.

I said that physics is the study of simple things, and this, too, may seem strange at first. Physics appears to be a complicated subject, because the ideas of physics are difficult for us to understand. Our brains were designed to understand hunting and gathering, mating and child-rearing: a world of medium-sized objects moving in three dimensions at moderate speeds. We are ill-equipped to comprehend the very small and the very large; things whose duration is measured in picoseconds or gigayears; particles that don't have position; forces and fields that we cannot see or touch, which we know of only because they affect things that we can see or touch. We think that physics is complicated because it is hard for us to understand, and because physics books are full of difficult mathematics. But the objects that physicists study are still basically simple objects. They are clouds of gas or tiny particles, or lumps of uniform matter like crystals, with almost endlessly repeated atomic patterns. They do not, at least by biological standards, have intricate working parts. Even large physical objects like stars consist of a rather limited array of parts, more or less haphazardly arranged. The behaviour of physical, nonbiological objects is so simple that it is feasible to use existing mathematical language to describe it, which is why physics books are full of mathematics.

Physics *books* may be complicated, but physics books, like cars and computers, are the product of biological objects – human brains. The objects and phenomena that a physics book describes are simpler than a single cell in the body of its author. And the author consists of trillions of those cells, many of them different from each other, organized with intricate architecture and precision-engineering into a working machine capable of writing a book. Our brains are no better equipped to handle extremes of complexity than extremes of size and the other difficult extremes of physics. The mathematics has not been invented for describing the total structure and behaviour of such an object as a physicist, or even of one of his cells. What we can do is understand some of the general principles of how living things work, and why they exist at all.

This was where we came in. We wanted to know why we, and all other complicated things, exist. And we can now answer that question in general terms, even without being able to comprehend the details of the complexity itself. To take an analogy, most of us don't understand in detail how an airliner works. Probably its builders don't comprehend it fully either: engine specialists don't in detail understand wings, and wing specialists understand engines only vaguely. Wing specialists don't even understand wings with full mathematical precision: they can predict how a wing will behave in turbulent conditions, only by examining a model in a wind tunnel or a computer simulation – the sort of thing a biologist might do to understand an animal. But however incompletely we understand how an airliner works, we all understand by what general process it came into existence. It was designed by humans on drawing boards. Then other humans made the bits from the drawings, then lots more humans (with the aid of other machines designed by humans) screwed, rivetted, welded or glued the bits together, each in its right place. The process by which an airliner came into existence is not fundamentally mysterious to us, because humans built it. The systematic putting together of parts to a purposeful design is something we know and understand, for we have experienced it at first hand, even if only with our childhood Meccano set.

What about our own bodies? Each one of us is a machine, like an airliner only much more complicated. Were we designed on a drawing board too, and were our parts assembled by a skilled engineer? The answer is no. It is a surprising answer, and we have known and understood it for only a century or so. When Charles Darwin first explained the matter, many people either wouldn't or couldn't grasp it. I myself flatly refused to believe Darwin's theory when I first heard about it as a child. Almost everybody throughout history, up to the second half of the nineteenth century, has firmly believed in the opposite – the Conscious Designer theory. Many people still do, perhaps because the true, Darwinian explanation of our own existence is still, remarkably, not a routine part of the curriculum of a general education. It is certainly very widely misunderstood.

The watchmaker of my title is borrowed from a famous treatise by the eighteenth-century theologian William Paley. His *Natural Theology – or Evidences of the Existence and Attributes of the Deity Collected from the Appearances of Nature*, published in 1802, is the best-known exposition of the 'Argument from Design', always the most influential of the arguments for the existence of a God. It is a book that I greatly admire, for in his own time its author succeeded in doing what I am struggling to do now. He had a point to make, he passionately believed in it, and he spared no effort to ram it home clearly. He had a proper reverence for the complexity of the living world, and he saw that it demands a very special kind of explanation. The only thing he got wrong – admittedly quite a big thing! – was the explanation itself. He gave the traditional religious answer to the riddle, but he articulated it more clearly and convincingly than anybody had before. The true explanation is utterly different, and it had to wait for one of the most revolutionary thinkers of all time, Charles Darwin.

Paley begins *Natural Theology* with a famous passage:

In crossing a heath, suppose I pitched my foot against a *stone*, and were asked how the stone came to be there; I might possibly answer, that, for anything I knew to the contrary, it had lain there for ever: nor would it perhaps be very easy to show the absurdity of this answer. But suppose I had found a *watch* upon the ground, and it should be inquired how the watch happened to be in that place; I should hardly think of the answer which I had before given, that for anything I knew, the watch might have always been there.

Paley here appreciates the difference between natural physical objects like stones, and designed and manufactured objects like watches. He goes on to expound the precision with which the cogs and springs of a watch are fashioned, and the intricacy with which they are put together. If we found an object such as a watch upon a heath, even if we didn't know how it had come into existence, its own precision and intricacy of design would force us to conclude

that the watch must have had a maker: that there must have existed, at some time, and at some place or other, an artificer or artificers, who formed it for the purpose which we find it actually to answer; who comprehended its construction, and designed its use.

Nobody could reasonably dissent from this conclusion, Paley insists, yet that is just what the atheist, in effect, does when he contemplates the works of nature, for:

every indication of contrivance, every manifestation of design, which existed in the watch, exists in the works of nature, with the difference, on the side of nature, of being greater or more, and that in a degree which exceeds all computation.

Paley drives his point home with beautiful and reverent descriptions of the dissected machinery of life, beginning with the human eye, a favourite example which Darwin was later to use. Paley compares the eye with a designed instrument such as a telescope, and concludes that 'there is precisely the same proof that the eye was made for vision, as there is that the telescope was made for assisting it'. The eye must have had a designer, just as the telescope had.

Paley's argument is made with passionate sincerity and is informed by the best biological scholarship of his day, but it is wrong, gloriously and utterly wrong. The analogy between telescope and eye, between watch and living organism, is false. All appearances to the contrary, the only watchmaker in nature is the blind forces of physics, albeit deployed in a very special way. A true watchmaker has foresight: he designs his cogs and springs, and plans their interconnections, with a future purpose in his mind's eye. Natural selection, the blind, unconscious, automatic process which Darwin discovered, and which we now know is the explanation for the existence and apparently purposeful form of all life, has no purpose in mind. It has no mind and no mind's eye. It does not plan for the future. It has no vision, no foresight, no sight at all. If it can be said to play the role of watchmaker in nature, it is the *blind* watchmaker.

I shall explain all this, and much else besides. But one thing I shall not do is belittle the wonder of the living 'watches' that so inspired Paley. On the contrary, I shall try to illustrate my feeling that here Paley could have gone even further. When it comes to feeling awe over living 'watches' I yield to nobody. I feel more in common with the Reverend William Paley than I do with the distinguished modern philosopher, a well-known atheist, with whom I once discussed the matter at dinner. I said that I could not imagine being an atheist at any time before 1859, when Darwin's *Origin of Species* was published. 'What about Hume?', replied the philosopher. 'How did Hume explain the organized complexity of the living world?', I asked. 'He didn't,' said the philosopher. 'Why does it need any special explanation?'

Paley knew that it needed a special explanation; Darwin knew it, and I suspect that in his heart of hearts my philosopher companion knew it too. In any case it will be my business to show it here. As for David Hume himself, it is sometimes said that that great Scottish philosopher disposed of the Argument from Design a century before Darwin. But what Hume did was criticize the logic of using apparent design in nature as *positive* evidence for the existence of a God.

He did not offer any *alternative* explanation for apparent design, but left the question open. An atheist before Darwin could have said, following Hume: 'I have no explanation for complex biological design. All I know is that God isn't a good explanation, so we must wait and hope that somebody comes up with a better one.' I can't help feeling that such a position, though logically sound, would have left one feeling pretty unsatisfied, and that although atheism might have been *logically* tenable before Darwin, Darwin made it possible to be an intellectually fulfilled atheist. I like to think that Hume would agree, but some of his writings suggest that he underestimated the complexity and beauty of biological design. The boy naturalist Charles Darwin could have shown him a thing or two about that, but Hume had been dead 40 years when Darwin enrolled in Hume's university of Edinburgh.

I have talked glibly of complexity, and of apparent design, as though it were obvious what these words mean. In a sense it is obvious – most people have an intuitive idea of what complexity means. But these notions, complexity and design, are so pivotal to this book that I must try to capture a little more precisely, in words, our feeling that there is something special about complex, and apparently designed, things.

So, what is a complex thing? How should we recognize it? In what sense is it true to say that a watch or an airliner or an earwig or a person is complex, but the moon is simple? The first point that might occur to us, as a necessary attribute of a complex thing, is that it has a heterogeneous structure. A pink milk pudding or blancmange is simple in the sense that, if we slice it in two, the two portions will have the same internal constitution: a blancmange is homogeneous. A car is heterogeneous: unlike a blancmange, almost any portion of the car is different from other portions. Two times half a car does not make a car. This will often amount to saying that a complex object, as opposed to a simple one, has many parts, these parts being of more than one kind.

Such heterogeneity, or 'many-partedness', may be a necessary condition, but it is not sufficient. Plenty of objects are many-parted and heterogeneous in internal structure, without being complex in the sense in which I want to use the term. Mont Blanc, for instance, consists of many different kinds of rock, all jumbled together in such a way that, if you sliced the mountain anywhere, the two portions would differ from each other in their internal constitution. Mont Blanc has a

heterogeneity of structure not possessed by a blancmange, but it is still not complex in the sense in which a biologist uses the term.

Let us try another tack in our quest for a definition of complexity, and make use of the mathematical idea of probability. Suppose we try out the following definition: a complex thing is something whose constituent parts are arranged in a way that is unlikely to have arisen by chance alone. To borrow an analogy from an eminent astronomer, if you take the parts of an airliner and jumble them up at random, the likelihood that you would happen to assemble a working Boeing is vanishingly small. There are billions of possible ways of putting together the bits of an airliner, and only one, or every few, of them would actually be an airliner. There are even more ways of putting together the scrambled parts of a human.

This approach to a definition of complexity is promising, but something more is still needed. There are billions of ways of throwing together the bits of Mont Blanc, it might be said, and only one of them is Mont Blanc. So what is it that makes the airliner and the human complicated, if Mont Blanc is simple? Any old jumbled collection of parts is unique and, *with hindsight*, is as improbable as any other. The scrapheap at an aircraft breaker's yard is unique. No two scrap-heaps are the same. If you start throwing fragments of aeroplanes into heaps, the odds of your happening to hit upon exactly the same arrangement of junk twice are just about as low as the odds of your throwing together a working airliner. So, why don't we say that a rubbish dump, or Mont Blanc, or the moon, is just as complex as an aeroplane or a dog, because in all these cases the arrangement of atoms is 'improbable'?

The combination lock on my bicycle has 4,096 different positions. Every one of these is equally 'improbable' in the sense that, if you spin the wheels at random, every one of the 4,096 positions is equally unlikely to turn up. I can spin the wheels at random, look at whatever number is displayed and exclaim with hindsight: 'How amazing. The odds against that number appearing are 4,096:1. A minor miracle!' That is equivalent to regarding the particular arrangement of rocks in a mountain, or of bits of metal in a scrap-heap, as 'complex'. But one of those 4,096 wheel positions really is interestingly unique: the combination 1207 is the only one that opens the lock. The uniqueness of 1207 has nothing to do with hindsight: it is specified in advance by the manufacturer. If you spun the wheels at random and happened to hit 1207 first time, you would be able to steal the bike, and it would seem a minor miracle. If you struck lucky on one of those multi-dialled combination locks on bank safes, it would seem a very major miracle, for the odds against it are many millions to one, and you would be able to steal a fortune.

Now, hitting upon the lucky number that opens the bank's safe is the equivalent, in our analogy, of hurling scrap metal around at random and happening to assemble a Boeing 747. Of all the millions of unique, and with hindsight equally improbable, positions of the combination lock, only one opens the lock. Similarly, of all the millions of unique, and with hindsight equally improbable, arrangements of a heap of junk, only one (or very few) will fly. The uniqueness of the arrangement that flies, or that opens the safe, is nothing to do with hindsight. It is specified in advance. The lock-manufacturer fixed the combination, and he has told the bank manager. The ability to fly is a property of an airliner that we specify in advance. If we see a plane in the air we can be sure that it was not assembled by randomly throwing scrap metal together, because we know that the odds against a random conglomeration's being able to fly are too great.

Now, if you consider all possible ways in which the

rocks of Mont Blanc could have been thrown together, it is true that only one of them would make Mont Blanc as we know it. But Mont Blanc as we know it is defined with hindsight. Any one of a very large number of ways of throwing rocks together would be labelled a mountain, and might have been named Mont Blanc. There is nothing special about the particular Mont Blanc that we know, nothing specified in advance, nothing equivalent to the plane taking off, or equivalent to the safe door swinging open and the money tumbling out.

What is the equivalent of the safe door swinging open, or the plane flying, in the case of a living body? Well, sometimes it is almost literally the same. Swallows fly. As we have seen, it isn't easy to throw together a flying machine. If you took all the cells of a swallow and put them together at random, the chance that the resulting object would fly is not, for everyday purposes, different from zero. Not all living things fly, but they do other things that are just as improbable, and just as specifiable in advance. Whales don't fly, but they do swim, and swim about as efficiently as swallows fly. The chance that a random conglomeration of whale cells would swim, let alone swim as fast and efficiently as a whale actually does swim, is negligible.

At this point, some hawk-eyed philosopher (hawks have very acute eyes — you couldn't make a hawk's eye by throwing lenses and light-sensitive cells together at random) will start mumbling something about a circular argument. Swallows fly but they don't swim, and whales swim but they don't fly. It is with hindsight that we decide whether to judge the success of our random conglomeration as a swimmer or as a flyer. Suppose we agree to judge its success as an Xer, and leave open exactly what X is until we have tried throwing cells together. The random lump of cells might turn out to be an efficient burrower like a mole or an efficient climber like a monkey. It might be very good at wind-surfing, or at clutching oily rags, or at walking in ever decreasing circles until it vanished. The list could go on and on. Or could it?

If the list really *could* go on and on, my hypothetical philosopher might have a point. If, no matter how randomly you threw matter around, the resulting conglomeration could often be said, with hindsight, to be good for *something*, then it would be true to say that I cheated over the swallow and the whale. But biologists can be much more specific than that about what would constitute being 'good for something'. The minimum requirement for us to recognize an object as an animal or plant is that it should succeed in making a living *of some sort* (more precisely that it, or at least some members of its kind, should live long enough to reproduce). It is true that there are quite a number of ways of making a living – flying, swimming, swinging through the trees, and so on. But, *however many ways there may be of being alive, it is certain that there are vastly more ways of being dead*, or rather not alive. You may throw cells together at random, over and over again for a billion years, and not once will you get a conglomeration that flies or swims or burrows or runs, or does *anything*, even badly, that could remotely be construed as working to keep itself alive.

This has been quite a long, drawn-out argument, and it is time to remind ourselves of how we got into it in the first place. We were looking for a precise way to express what we mean when we refer to something as complicated. We were trying to put a finger on what it is that humans and moles and earthworms and airliners and watches have in common with each other, but not with blancmange, or Mont Blanc, or the moon. The answer we have arrived at is that complicated things have some quality, specifiable in advance, that is highly unlikely to have been acquired by random chance alone. In the case of living things, the quality that is specified in advance is, in some sense, 'proficiency'; either proficiency in a particular ability such as flying, as an aero-engineer might admire it; or proficiency in something more general, such as the ability to stave off death, or the ability to propagate genes in reproduction.

Staving off death is a thing that you have to work at. Left to itself – and that is what it is when it dies – the body tends to revert to a state of equilibrium with its environment. If you measure some quantity such as the temperature, the acidity, the water content or the electrical potential in a living body, you will typically find that it is markedly different from the corresponding measure in the surroundings. Our bodies, for instance, are usually hotter than our surroundings, and in cold climates they have to work hard to maintain the differential. When we die the work stops, the temperature differential starts to disappear, and we end up the same temperature as our surroundings. Not all animals work so hard to avoid coming into equilibrium with their surrounding temperature, but all animals do *some* comparable work. For instance, in a dry country, animals and plants work to maintain the fluid content of their cells, work against a natural tendency for water to flow from them into the dry outside world. If they fail they die. More generally, if living things didn't work actively to prevent it, they would eventually merge into their surroundings, and cease to exist as autonomous beings. That is what happens when they die.

With the exception of artificial machines, which we have already agreed to count as honorary living things, nonliving things don't work in this sense. They accept the forces that tend to bring them into equilibrium with their surroundings. Mont Blanc, to be sure, has existed for a long time, and probably will exist for a while yet, but it does not work to stay in existence. When rock comes to rest under the influence of gravity it just stays there. No work has to be done to keep it there. Mont Blanc exists, and it will go on existing until it wears away or an earthquake knocks it over. It doesn't take steps to repair wear and tear, or to right itself when it is knocked over, the way a living body does. It just obeys the ordinary laws of physics.

Is this to deny that living things obey the laws of physics? Certainly not. There is no reason to think that the laws of physics are violated in living matter. There is nothing supernatural, no 'life force' to rival the fundamental forces of physics. It is just that if

you try to use the laws of physics, in a naïve way, to

understand the behaviour of a *whole* living body, you will find that you don't get very far. The body is a complex thing with many constituent parts, and to understand its behaviour you must apply the laws of physics to its parts, not to the whole. The behaviour of the body as a whole will then emerge as a consequence of interactions of the parts.

Take the laws of motion, for instance. If you throw a dead bird into the air it will describe a graceful parabola, exactly as physics books say it should, then come to rest on the ground and stay there. It behaves as a solid body of a particular mass and wind resistance ought to behave. But if you throw a live bird in the air it will not describe a parabola and come to rest on the ground. It will fly away, and may not touch land this side of the county boundary. The reason is that it has muscles which work to resist gravity and other physical forces bearing upon the whole body. The laws of physics are being obeyed within every cell of the muscles. The result is that the muscles move the wings in such a way that the bird stays aloft. The bird is not violating the law of gravity. It is constantly being pulled downwards by gravity, but its wings are performing active work – obeying laws of physics within its muscles – to keep it aloft in spite of the force of gravity. We shall think that it defies a physical law if we are naïve enough to treat it simply as a structureless lump of matter with a certain mass and wind resistance. It is only when we remember that it has many internal parts, all obeying laws of physics at their own level, that we understand the behaviour of the whole body. This is not, of course, a peculiarity of living things. It applies to all man-made machines, and potentially applies to any complex, many-parted object.

This brings me to the final topic that I want to discuss in this rather philosophical chapter, the problem of what we mean by explanation. We have seen what we are going to mean by a complex thing. But what kind of explanation will satisfy us if we wonder how a complicated machine, or living body, works? The answer is the one that we arrived at in the previous paragraph. If we wish to understand how a machine or living body works, we look to its component parts and ask how they interact with each other. If there is a complex thing that we do not yet understand, we can come to understand it in terms of simpler parts that we do already understand.

If I ask an engineer how a steam engine works, I

have a pretty fair idea of the general kind of answer

that would satisfy me. Like Julian Huxley I should definitely not be impressed if the engineer said it was propelled by '*force locomotif*'. And if he started boring on about the whole being greater than the sum of its parts, I would interrupt him: 'Never mind about that, tell me how it *works*.' What I would want to hear is something about how the parts of an engine interact with each other to produce the behaviour of the whole engine. I would initially be prepared to accept an explanation in terms of quite large subcomponents, whose own internal structure and behaviour might be quite complicated and, as yet, unexplained. The units of an initially satisfying explanation could have names like fire-box, boiler, cylinder, piston, steam governor. The engineer would assert, without explanation initially, what each of these units does. I would accept this for the moment, without asking how each unit does its own particular thing. *Given* that the units each do their particular thing, I can then understand how they interact to make the whole engine work.

Of course, I am then at liberty to ask how each part works. Having previously accepted the *fact* that the steam governor regulates the flow of steam, and having used this fact in my understanding of the behaviour of the whole engine, I now turn my curiosity on the 23 steam governor itself. I now want to understand how it achieves its own behaviour, in terms of its own internal parts. There is a hierarchy of subcomponents within components. We explain the behaviour of a component at any given level, in terms of interactions between subcomponents whose own internal organization, for the moment, is taken for granted. We peel our way down the hierarchy, until we reach units so simple that, for everyday purposes, we no longer feel the need to ask questions about them. Rightly or wrongly, for instance, most of us are happy about the properties of rigid rods of iron, and we are prepared to use them as units of explanation of more complex machines that contain them.

Physicists, of course, do not take iron rods for granted. They ask why they are rigid, and they continue the hierarchical peeling for several more layers yet, down to fundamental particles and quarks. But life is too short for most of us to follow them. For any given level of complex organization, satisfying explanations may normally be attained if we peel the hierarchy down one or two layers from our starting layer, but not more. The behaviour of a motor car is explained in terms of cylinders, carburettors and sparking plugs. It is true that each one of these components rests atop a pyramid of explanations at lower levels. But if you asked me how a motor car worked you would think me somewhat pompous if I answered in terms of Newton's laws and the laws of thermodynamics, and downright obscurantist if I answered in terms of fundamental particles. It is doubtless true that at bottom the behaviour of a motor car is to be explained in terms of interactions between fundamental particles. But it is much more useful to explain it in terms of interactions between pistons, cylinders and sparking plugs.

The behaviour of a computer can be explained in terms of interactions between semiconductor electronic gates, and the behaviour of these, in turn, is explained by physicists at yet lower levels. But, for most purposes, you would in practice be wasting your time if you tried to understand the behaviour of the whole computer at either of those levels. There are too many electronic gates and too many interconnections between them. A satisfying explanation has to be in terms of a manageably small number of interactions. This is why, if we want to understand the workings of computers, we prefer a preliminary explanation in terms of about half a dozen major subcomponents – memory, processing mill, backing store, control unit, input—output handler, etc. Having grasped the interactions between the half-dozen major components, we then may wish to ask questions about the internal organization of these major components. Only specialist engineers are likely to go down to the level of AND gates and NOR gates, and only physicists will go down further, to the level of how electrons behave in a semiconducting medium.

For those that like '-ism' sorts of names, the aptest name for my approach to understanding how things work is probably 'hierarchical reductionism'. If you read trendy intellectual magazines, you may have noticed that 'reductionism' is one of those things, like sin, that is only mentioned by people who are against it. To call oneself a reductionist will sound, in some circles, a bit like admitting to eating babies. But, just as nobody actually eats babies, so nobody is really a reductionist in any sense worth being against. The nonexistent reductionist – the sort that everybody is against, but who exists only in their imaginations – tries to explain complicated things *directly* in terms of the *smallest* parts, even, in some extreme versions of the myth, as the *sum* of the parts! The hierarchical reductionist, on the other hand, explains a complex entity at any particular level in the hierarchy of organization, in terms of entities only one level down the hierarchy; entities which, themselves, are likely to be complex enough to need further reducing to their own component parts; and so on. It goes without saying – though the mythical, baby-eating reductionist is reputed to deny this – that the kinds of explanations which are suitable at high levels in the hierarchy are quite different from the kinds of explanations which are suitable at lower levels. This was the point of explaining cars in terms of carburettors rather than quarks. But the hierarchical reductionist believes that carburettors are explained in terms of smaller units . . ., which are explained in terms of smaller units . . ., which are ultimately explained in terms of the smallest of fundamental particles. Reductionism, in this sense, is just another name for an honest desire to understand how things work.

We began this section by asking what kind of explanation for complicated things would satisfy us. We have just considered the question from the point of view of mechanism: how does it work? We concluded that the behaviour of a complicated thing should be explained in terms of interactions between its component parts, considered as successive layers of an orderly hierarchy. But another kind of question is how 27 the complicated thing came into existence in the first place. This is the question that this whole book is particularly concerned with, so I won't say much more about it here. I shall just mention that the same general principle applies as for understanding mechanism. A complicated thing is one whose existence we do not feel inclined to take for granted, because it is too 'improbable'. It could not have come into existence in a single act of chance. We shall explain its coming into existence as a consequence of gradual, cumulative, step-by-step transformations from simpler things, from primordial objects sufficiently simple to have come into being by chance. Just as 'big-step reductionism' cannot work as an explanation of mechanism, and must be replaced by a series of small step-by-step peelings down through the hierarchy, so we can't explain a complex thing as *originating* in a single step. We must again resort to a series of small steps, this time arranged sequentially in time.

In his beautifully written book, *The Creation*, the Oxford physical chemist Peter Atkins begins:

I shall take your mind on a journey. It is a journey of comprehension, taking us to the edge of space, time, and understanding. On it I shall argue that there is nothing that cannot be understood, that there is nothing that cannot be explained, and that everything is extraordinarily simple . . . A great deal of the universe does not need any explanation. Elephants, for instance. Once molecules have learnt to compete and to create other molecules in their own image, elephants, and things resembling elephants, will in due course be found roaming through the countryside.

Atkins assumes the evolution of complex things – the subject matter of this book – to be inevitable once the appropriate physical conditions have been set up. He asks what the minimum necessary physical conditions are, what is the minimum amount of design work that a very lazy Creator would have to do, in order to see to it that the universe and, later, elephants and other complex things, would one day come into existence. The answer, from his point of view as a physical scientist, is that the Creator could be infinitely lazy. The fundamental original units that we need to postulate, in order to understand the coming into existence of everything, either consist of literally nothing (according to some physicists), or (according to other physicists) they are units of the utmost simplicity, far too simple to need anything so grand as deliberate Creation.

Atkins says that elephants and complex things do

not need any explanation. But that is because he is a physical scientist, who takes for granted the biologists' theory of evolution. He doesn't really mean that elephants don't need an explanation; rather that he is satisfied that biologists can explain elephants, provided they are allowed to take certain facts of physics for granted. His task as a physical scientist, therefore, is to justify our taking those facts for granted. This he succeeds in doing. My position is complementary. I am a biologist. I take the facts of physics, the facts of the world of simplicity, for granted. If physicists still don't agree over whether those simple facts are yet understood, that is not my problem. My task is to explain elephants, and the world of complex things, in terms of the simple things that physicists either understand, or are working on. The physicist's problem is the problem of ultimate origins and ultimate natural laws. The biologist's problem is the problem of complexity. The biologist tries to explain the workings, and the coming into existence, of complex things, in terms of simpler things. He can regard his task as done when he has arrived at entities so simple that they can safely be handed over to physicists.

I am aware that my characterization of a complex object – statistically improbable in a direction that is specified not with hindsight – may seem idiosyncratic. So, too, may seem my characterization of physics as the study of simplicity. If you prefer some other way of defining complexity, I don't care and I would be happy to go along with your definition for the sake of discussion. But what I do care about is that, whatever we choose to *call* the quality of being statistically-improbable-in-a-direction-specified-without-hindsight, it is an important quality that needs a special effort of explanation. It is the quality that characterizes biological objects as opposed to the objects of physics. The kind of explanation we come up with must not contradict the laws of physics. Indeed it will make use of the laws of physics, and nothing more than the laws of physics. But it will deploy the laws of physics in a special way that is not ordinarily discussed in physics textbooks. That special way is Darwin's way.

Many people find it hard to believe that something like the eye, Paley's favourite example, so complex and well designed, with so many interlocking working parts, could have arisen from small beginnings by a gradual series of step-by-step changes. I consider the step-by-step evolution of the eye in Chapter 5 of my book, *Climbing Mount Improbable*. We begin this brief treatment by answering the following two questions:

1. Could the human eye have arisen directly from no eye at all, in a single step?

2. Could the human eye have arisen directly from something slightly different from itself, something that we may call X?

The answer to Question 1 is clearly a decisive *no*. The odds against a 'yes' answer for questions like Question 1 are many billions of times greater than the number of atoms in the universe. It would need a gigantic and vanishingly improbable leap, equivalent to spontaneously assembling an airliner from a heap of junk. The answer to Question 2 is equally clearly *yes*, provided only that the difference between the modern eye and its immediate predecessor X is sufficiently small. Provided, in other words, that they are sufficiently close to one another in the hypothetical space of all possible structures. If the answer to Question 2 for any particular degree of difference is no, all we have to do is repeat the question for a smaller degree of difference. Carry on doing this until we find a degree of difference sufficiently small to give us a 'yes' answer to Question 2.

X is *defined* as something very like a human eye, sufficiently similar that the human eye could plausibly have arisen by a single alteration in X. If you have a mental picture of X and you find it implausible that the human eye could have arisen directly from it, this simply means that you have chosen the wrong X. Make your mental picture of X progressively more like a human eye, until you find an X that you *do* find plausible as an immediate predecessor to the human eye. There has to be one for you, even if your idea of what is plausible may be more, or less, cautious than mine!

Now, having found an X such that the answer to Question 2 is yes, we apply the same question to X itself. By the same reasoning we must conclude that X could plausibly have arisen, directly by a single change, from something slightly different again, which we may call X'. Obviously we can then trace X' back to something else slightly different from it, X", and so on. By interposing a large enough series of Xs, we can derive the human eye from something not slightly different from itself but *very* different from itself. We can 'walk' a large distance across 'animal space', and our move will be plausible provided we take small enough steps. We are now in a position to answer a third question.

3. Is there a continuous series of Xs connecting the modern human eye to a state with no eye at all?

It seems to me clear that the answer has to be yes, provided only that we allow ourselves a *sufficiently large* series of Xs. You might feel that 1,000 Xs is ample, but if you need more steps to make the total transition plausible in your mind, simply allow yourself to assume 10,000 Xs. And if 10,000 is not enough for you, allow yourself 100,000, and so on. Obviously the available time imposes an upper ceiling on this game, for there can be only one X per generation. In practice the question therefore resolves itself into: Has there been enough time for enough successive generations? We can't give a precise answer to the number of generations that would be necessary. What we do know is that geological time is awfully long. Just to give you an idea of the order of magnitude we are talking about, the number of generations that separate us from our earliest ancestors is certainly measured in the thousands of millions. Given, say, a hundred million Xs, we should be able to construct a plausible series of tiny gradations linking a human eye to just about anything!

So far, by a process of more-or-less abstract reasoning, we have concluded that there is a series of imaginable Xs, each sufficiently similar to its neighbours that it could plausibly turn into one of its neighbours, the whole series linking the human eye back to no eye at all. But we still haven't demonstrated that it is plausible that this series of Xs actually existed. We have two more questions to answer.

4. Considering each member of the series of hypothetical Xs connecting the human eye to no eye at all, is it plausible that every one of them was made available by random mutation of its predecessor?

This is really a question about embryology, not genetics. Mutation has to work by modifying the existing 35 processes of embryonic development. It is arguable that certain kinds of embryonic process are highly amenable to variation in certain directions, recalcitrant to variation in others. The smaller the change you postulate, the smaller the difference between X" and X', the more embryologically plausible is the mutation concerned. Any *particular* large mutation is inherently less probable than any particular small mutation. Whatever problems may be raised by Question 4, then, we can at least see that the smaller we make the difference between any given X' and X", the smaller will be the problems. My feeling is that, provided the difference between neighbouring intermediates in our series leading to the eye is *sufficiently small*, the necessary mutations are almost bound to be forthcoming. We are, after all, always talking about minor quantitative changes in an existing embryonic process. Remember that, however complicated the embryological status quo may be in any given generation, each mutational *change* in the status quo can be very small and simple.

We have one final question to answer:

5. Considering each member of the series of Xs connecting the human eye to no eye at all, is it plausible

that every one of them worked sufficiently well that it assisted the survival and reproduction of the animals concerned?

Rather oddly, some people have thought that the answer to this question is a self-evident 'no'. For instance, I quote from Francis Hitching's book of 1982 called *The Neck of the Giraffe or Where Darwin Went Wrong*. I could have quoted basically the same words from almost any Jehovah's Witness tract, but I choose this book because a reputable publisher (Pan Books Ltd) saw fit to publish it, despite a very large number of errors which would quickly have been spotted if an unemployed biology graduate, or indeed undergraduate, had been asked to glance through the manuscript. (My favourites, if you'll indulge me just two in-jokes, are the conferring of a knighthood on Professor John Maynard Smith, and the description of Professor Ernst Mayr, that eloquent and most unmathematical arch-critic of mathematical genetics, as 'the high priest' of mathematical genetics.)

For the eye to work the following minimum perfectly coordinated steps have to take place (there are many others happening simultaneously, but even a grossly simplified description is enough to point up the problems for

Darwinian theory). The eye must be clean and moist, maintained in this state by the interaction of the tear gland and movable eyelids, whose eyelashes also act as a crude filter against the sun. The light then passes through a small transparent section of the protective outer coating (the *cornea*), and continues via a *lens* which focuses it on the back of the *retina*. Here 130 million light-sensitive rods and cones cause photochemical reactions which transform the light into electrical impulses. Some 1,000 million of these are transmitted every second, by means that are not properly understood, to a brain which then takes appropriate action.

Now it is quite evident that if the slightest thing goes wrong *en route* – if the cornea is fuzzy, or the pupil fails to dilate, or the lens becomes opaque, or the focusing goes wrong – then a recognizable image is not formed. The eye either functions as a whole, or not at all. So how did it come to evolve by slow, steady, infinitesimally small Darwinian improvements? Is it really plausible that thousands upon thousands of lucky chance mutations happened coincidentally so that the lens and the retina, which cannot work without each other, evolved in synchrony? What survival value can there be in an eye that doesn't see?

This remarkable argument is very frequently made, presumably because people *want* to believe its conclusion. Consider the statement that 'if the slightest thing goes wrong . . . if the focusing goes wrong . . . a recognizable image is not formed'. The odds cannot be far from 50/50 that you are reading these words through glass lenses. Take them off and look around. Would you agree that 'a recognizable image is not formed'? If you are male, the odds are about 1 in 12 that you are colourblind. You may well be astigmatic. It is not unlikely that, without glasses, your vision is a misty blur. One of today's most distinguished (though not yet knighted) evolutionary theorists so seldom cleans his glasses that his vision is probably a misty blur anyway, but he seems to get along pretty well and, by his own account, he used to play a mean game of monocular squash. If you have lost your glasses, it may be that you upset your friends by failing to recognize them in the street. But you yourself would be even more upset if somebody said to you: 'Since your vision is now not absolutely perfect, you might as well go around with your eyes tight shut until you find your glasses again.' Yet that is essentially what the author of the passage I have quoted is suggesting.

He also states, as though it were obvious, that the lens and the retina cannot work without each other. On what authority? Someone close to me has had a cataract operation in both eyes. She has no lenses in her eyes at all. Without glasses she couldn't even begin to play lawn tennis or aim a rifle. But she assures me that you are far better off with a lensless eye than with no eye at all. You can tell if you are about to walk into a wall or another person. If you were a wild creature, you could certainly use your lensless eye to detect the looming shape of a predator, and the direction from which it was approaching. In a primitive world where some creatures had no eyes at all and others had lensless eyes, the ones with lensless eyes would have all sorts of advantages. And there is a continuous series of Xs, such that each tiny improvement in sharpness of image, from swimming blur to perfect human vision, plausibly increases the organism's chances of surviving.

The book goes on to quote Stephen Jay Gould, the noted Harvard palaeontologist, as saying:

We avoid the excellent question, What good is 5 per cent of an eye? by arguing that the possessor of such an incipient structure did not use it for sight.

An ancient animal with 5 per cent of an eye might indeed have used it for something other than sight, but it seems to me at least as likely that it used it for 5 per cent vision. And actually I don't think it is an excellent question. Vision that is 5 per cent as good as yours or mine is very much worth having in comparison with no vision at all. So is 1 per cent vision better than total blindness. And 6 per cent is better than 5, 7 per cent better than 6, and so on up the gradual, continuous series.

This kind of problem has worried some people interested in animals that gain protection from predators by 'mimicry'. Stick insects look like sticks and so are saved from being eaten by birds. Leaf insects look like leaves. Many edible species of butterfly gain protection by resembling noxious or poisonous species.

We use the word 'mimicry' for these cases, not because we think that the animals consciously imitate other things, but because natural selection has favoured those individuals whose bodies were mistaken for other things. To put it another way, ancestors of stick insects that did not resemble sticks did not leave descendants. The German–American geneticist Richard Goldschmidt is the most distinguished of those who have argued that the *early* evolution of such resemblances could not have been favoured by natural selection. As Gould, an admirer of Goldschmidt, said of dung-mimicking insects: 'can there be any edge in looking 5 per cent like a turd?' Largely through

Gould's influence, it has recently become fashionable to say that Goldschmidt was underrated in his own lifetime, and that he really has much to teach us. Here is a sample of his reasoning.

Ford speaks ... of any mutation which chances to give a 'remote resemblance' to a more protected species, from which some advantage, however slight, might accrue. We must ask how remote the resemblance can be to have select-ive value. Can we really assume that the birds and monkeys and also mantids are such wonderful observers (or that some very clever ones among them are) to notice a 'remote' resemblance and be repelled by it? I think that this is asking too much.

Such sarcasm ill becomes anybody on the shaky ground that Goldschmidt here treads. *Wonderful* observers? Very *clever* ones among them? Anybody would think the birds and monkeys *benefited* from being fooled by the remote resemblance! Goldschmidt might rather have said: 'Can we really assume that the birds, etc. are such *poor* observers (or that some very stupid ones among them are)?' Nevertheless, there is a real dilemma here. The initial resemblance of the ancestral stick insect to a stick must have been very remote. A bird would need extremely *poor* vision to be fooled by it. Yet the resemblance of a modern stick insect to a stick is marvellously good, down to the last fine details of fake buds and leaf-scars. The birds whose selective predation put the finishing touches to their evolution must, at least collectively, have had excellently *good* vision. They must have been extremely hard to fool, otherwise the insects would not have evolved to become as perfect mimics as they are: they would have remained relatively imperfect mimics. How can we resolve this apparent contradiction?

One kind of answer suggests that bird vision has been improving over the same evolutionary timespan as insect camouflage. Perhaps, to be a little facetious, an ancestral insect that looked only 5 per cent like a turd would have fooled an ancestral bird with only 5 per cent vision. But that is not the kind of answer I want to give. I suspect, indeed, that the whole process of evolution, from remote resemblance to near perfect mimicry, has gone on, rather rapidly, many times over in different insect groups, during the whole long period that bird vision has been just about as good as it is today.

Another kind of answer that has been offered to the dilemma is the following. Perhaps each species of bird or monkey has poor vision and latches on to just one limited aspect of an insect. Maybe one predator species notices only the colour, another only the shape, another only the texture, and so on. Then an insect that resembles a stick in only one limited respect will fool one kind of predator, even though it is eaten by all other kinds of predators. As evolution progresses, more and more features of resemblance are added to the repertoire of the insects. The final multifaceted perfection of mimicry has been put together by the summed natural selection provided by many different species of predators. No one predator sees the whole perfection of mimicry, only we do that.

This seems to imply that only we are 'clever' enough to see the mimicry in all its glory. Not only because of this human snobbishness, I prefer yet another explanation. This is that, no matter how good any one predator's vision may be under some conditions, it can be exceedingly poor under other conditions. We can easily, in fact, appreciate from our own familiar experience the whole spectrum from exceedingly poor vision to excellent vision. If I am looking directly at a stick insect, 8 inches in front of my nose and in strong daylight, I shall not be fooled by it. I shall notice the long legs hugging the line of the trunk. I may spot the unnatural symmetry which a real stick would not have.

But if I, with the very same eyes and brain, am walking through a forest at dusk, I may well fail to distinguish almost any dull-coloured insect from the twigs that abound everywhere. The image of the insect may pass over the edge of my retina rather than the more acute central region. The insect may be 50 yards away, and so make only a tiny image on my retina. The light may be so poor that I can hardly see anything at all anyway.

In fact, it doesn't matter *how* remote, how poor is the resemblance of an insect to a stick, there must be *some* level of twilight, or some degree of distance away from the eye, or some degree of distraction of the predator's attention, such that even a very good eye will be fooled by the remote resemblance. If you don't find that plausible for some particular example that you have imagined, just turn down the imaginary light a bit, or move a bit further away from the imaginary object! The point is that many an insect was saved by an exceedingly slight resemblance to a twig or a leaf or a fall of dung, on occasions when it was far away from a predator, or on occasions when the predator was looking at it at dusk, or looking at it through a fog, or looking at it while distracted by a receptive female. And many an insect was saved, perhaps from the very same predator, by an uncannily close resemblance to a twig, on occasions when the predator happened to be seeing it at relatively close range and in a good light. The important thing about light intensity, distance of insect from predator, distance of image from centre of retina, and similar variables, is that they are all *continuous* variables. They vary by insensible degrees all the way from the extreme of invisibility to the extreme of visibility. Such continuous variables foster continuous and gradual evolution.

Richard Goldschmidt's problem – which was one of a set that made him resort, for most of his professional life, to the extreme belief that evolution takes great leaps rather than small steps – turns out to be no problem at all. And incidentally, we have also demonstrated to ourselves, yet again, that 5 per cent vision is better than no vision at all. The quality of my vision right at the edge of my retina is probably even poorer than 5 per cent of the quality at the centre of my retina, however you care to measure quality. Yet I can still detect the presence of a large lorry or bus out of the extreme corner of my eye. Since I ride a bicycle to work every day this fact has quite probably saved my life. I notice the difference on those occasions when it is raining and I wear a hat. The quality of our vision on a dark night must be far poorer than 5 per cent of what it is at midday. Yet many an ancestor was probably saved through seeing something that really mattered, a sabre-tooth 'tiger' perhaps, or a precipice, in the middle of the night.

Every one of us knows from personal experience, for example on dark nights, that there is an insensibly graded continuous series running all the way from total blindness up to perfect vision, and that every step along this series confers significant benefits. By looking at the world through progressively defocused and focused binoculars, we can quickly convince ourselves that there is a graded series of focusing quality, each step in the series being an improvement over the previous one. By progressively turning the colour-balance knob of a colour television set, we can convince ourselves that there is a graded series of progressive improvement from black and white to full colour vision. The iris diaphragm that opens and shuts the pupil prevents us from being dazzled in bright light, while allowing us to see in dim light. We all experience what it is like not to have an iris diaphragm, when we are momentarily dazzled by oncoming car headlights. Unpleasant, and even dangerous, as this dazzling can be, it still doesn't mean that the whole eye ceases to work! The claim that 'The eye either functions as a whole, or not at all' turns out to be, not merely false but self-evidently false to anybody who thinks for two seconds about his own familiar experience.

Anti-evolution propaganda is full of alleged examples of complex systems that 'could not possibly' have passed through a gradual series of intermediates, a rather pathetic 'Argument from Personal Incredulity'. Immediately after the section on the eye, for example, *The Neck of the Giraffe* goes on to discuss the bombardier beetle, which

squirts a lethal mixture of hydroquinone and hydrogen peroxide into the face of its enemy. These two chemicals, when mixed together, literally explode. So in order to store them inside its body, the Bombardier Beetle has evolved a chemical inhibitor to make them harmless. At the moment the beetle squirts the liquid out of its tail, an anti-inhibitor is added to make the mixture explosive once again. The chain of events that could have led to the evolution of such a complex, coordinated and subtle process is beyond biological explanation on a simple step-by-step basis. The slightest alteration in the chemical balance would result immediately in a race of exploded beetles.

A biochemist colleague has kindly provided me with
a bottle of hydrogen peroxide, and enough hydro-

quinone for 50 bombardier beetles. I am now about to mix the two together. According to the above, they will explode in my face. Here goes . . .

Well, I'm still here. I poured the hydrogen peroxide into the hydroquinone, and absolutely nothing happened. It didn't even get warm. Of course I knew it wouldn't: I'm not that foolhardy! The statement that 'these two chemicals, when mixed together, literally explode', is, quite simply, false, although it is regularly repeated throughout creationist literature. If you are curious about the bombardier beetle, by the way, what actually happens is as follows. It is true that it squirts a scaldingly hot mixture of hydrogen peroxide and hydroquinone at enemies. But hydrogen peroxide and hydroquinone don't react violently together unless a catalyst is *added*. This is what the bombardier beetle does. As for the evolutionary precursors of the system, both hydrogen peroxide and various kinds of quinones are used for other purposes in body chemistry. The bombardier beetle's ancestors simply pressed into different service chemicals that already happened to be around. That's often how evolution works.

On the same page of the book as the bombardier beetle passage is the question: 'What use would be . . . half a lung? Natural selection would surely eliminate   49 creatures with such oddities, not preserve them.' In a healthy adult human, each of the two lungs is divided into about 300 million tiny chambers, at the tips of a branching system of tubes that resembles a tree. As you go up the tree, with each branching the number of twig tips successively doubles. In order to provide 300 million twig tips, only 29 successive doublings would be required. Note that there is a continuous gradation from a single chamber to 300 million tiny chambers, each step in the gradation being provided by another two-way branching. This transition can be accomplished in 29 branchings, which we may naïvely think of as a stately walk of 29 steps across genetic space.

In the lungs, the result of all this branching is that the surface area inside each lung is rather more than 70 square yards. Area is the important variable for a lung, for it is area that determines the rate at which oxygen can be taken in, and waste carbon dioxide pushed out. Now, the thing about area is that it is a *continuous* variable. Area is not one of those things that you either have or you don't. It is a thing that you can have a little bit more of, or a little bit less of. More than most things, lung area lends itself to *gradual*, step-by-step change, all the way from 0 square yards up to 70 square yards.

There are plenty of surgical patients walking around with only one lung, and some of them are down to a third of normal lung area. They may be walking, but they aren't walking very far, nor very fast. That is the point. The effect of gradually reducing lung area is not an absolute, all-or-none effect on survival. It is a gradual, continuously varying effect of how far you can walk, and how fast. A gradual, continuously varying effect, indeed, on how long you can expect to live. Death doesn't suddenly arrive below a particular threshold lung area! It becomes gradually more probable as lung area decreases below an optimum (and as it increases above the same optimum, for different reasons connected with economic waste).

The first of our ancestors to develop lungs almost certainly lived in water. We can get an idea of how they might have breathed by looking at modern fish. Most modern fish breathe in water with gills, but many species living in foul, swampy water supplement this by gulping air at the surface. They use the internal chamber of the mouth as a kind of crude proto-lung, and this cavity is sometimes enlarged into a breathing pocket rich in blood vessels. As we've seen, there is no problem in imagining a continuous series of Xs connecting a single pocket to 51 a branching set of 300 million pockets as in a modern human lung.

Interestingly, many modern fish have kept their pocket single, and use it for a completely different purpose. Although it probably began as a lung, over the course of evolution it has become the swimbladder, an ingenious device with which the fish maintains itself as a hydrostat in permanent equilibrium. An animal without an air bladder inside it is normally slightly heavier than water, so sinks to the bottom. This is why sharks have to swim continuously to stop themselves sinking. An animal with large air pockets inside it, like us with our great lungs, tends to rise to the surface. Somewhere in the middle of this continuum, an animal with an air bladder of exactly the right size neither sinks nor rises, but floats steadily in effortless equilibrium. This is the trick that modern fish, other than sharks, have perfected. Unlike sharks, they don't waste energy preventing themselves from sinking. Their fins and tail are freed for guidance and rapid propulsion. They no longer rely on outside air to fill the bladder, but have special glands for manufacturing gas. Using these glands and other means, they accurately regulate the volume of gas in the bladder, and hence keep themselves in precise hydrostatic equilibrium.

Several species of modern fish can leave the water. An extreme is the Indian climbing perch, which hardly ever goes into the water. It has independently evolved a quite different kind of lung from that of our ancestors – an air chamber surrounding the gills. Other fish live basically in water but make brief forays out of it. This is probably what our ancestors did. The thing about forays is that their duration can vary continuously, all the way down to zero. If you are a fish who basically lives and breathes in water, but who occasionally ventures on land, perhaps to cross from one mud puddle to another thereby surviving a drought, you might benefit not just from half a lung but from one-hundredth of a lung. It doesn't matter *how* small your primordial lung is, there must be *some* time out of water that you can just endure with the lung, which is a little bit longer than you could have endured without the lung. Time is a continuous variable. There is no hard-and-fast divide between water-breathing and air-breathing animals. Different animals may spend 99 per cent of their time in water, 98 per cent, 97 per cent, and so on all the way to 0 per cent. At every step of the way, some fractional increase in lung area will be an advantage. There is continuity, gradualism, all the way.

The idea of tiny changes cumulated over many steps is an immensely powerful idea, capable of explaining an enormous range of things that would be otherwise inexplicable. How did snake venom get its start? Many animals bite, and any animal's spit contains proteins which, if they get into a wound, may cause an allergic reaction. Even so-called non-venomous snakes can give bites that cause a painful reaction in some people. There is a continuous, graded series from ordinary spit to deadly venom.

How did ears get their start? Any piece of skin can detect vibrations if they come in contact with vibrating objects. This is a natural out-growth of the sense of touch. Natural selection could easily have enhanced this faculty by gradual degrees until it was sensitive enough to pick up very *slight* contact vibrations. At this point it would automatically have been sensitive enough to pick up *airborne* vibrations of sufficient loudness and/or sufficient nearness of origin. Natural selection would then favour the evolution of special organs – ears – for picking up airborne vibrations originating from steadily increasing distances. It is easy to see that there would have been a continuous trajectory of step-by-step improvement, all the way.

Five per cent vision is better than no vision at all. Five per cent hearing is better than no hearing at all. Five per cent flight efficiency is better than no flight at all. It is thoroughly believable that every organ or apparatus that we actually see is the product of a smooth trajectory through a set of intermediates, a trajectory in which every intermediate stage assisted survival and reproduction. Wherever we have an X in a real live animal, where X is some organ too complex to have arisen by chance in a single step, then according to the theory of evolution by natural selection it must be the case that a fraction of an X is better than no X at all; and two fractions of an X must be better than one; and a whole X must be better than nine-tenths of an X. I have no trouble at all in accepting that these statements are true of eyes, ears including bat ears, wings, camouflaged and mimicking insects, snake jaws, stings, cuckoo habits and all the other examples trotted out in anti-evolution propaganda. No doubt there are plenty of *conceivable* Xs for which these statements would *not* be true, plenty of conceivable evolutionary pathways for which the intermediates would *not* be improvements on their predecessors. But those Xs are not found in the real world.

Darwin wrote (in *The Origin of Species*):

If it could be demonstrated that any complex organ existed which could not possibly have been formed by numerous, successive, slight modifications, my theory would absolutely break down.

One hundred and twenty-five years on, we know a lot more about animals and plants than Darwin did, and still not a single case is known to me of a complex organ that could not have been formed by numerous successive slight modifications. I do not believe that such a case will ever be found. If it is – it'll have to be a *really* complex organ, and you have to be sophisticated about what you mean by 'slight' – I shall cease to believe in Darwinism.

Sometimes the history of gradual, intermediate stages is clearly written into the shape of modern animals, even taking the form of outright imperfections in the final design. Stephen Gould, in his excellent essay on *The Panda's Thumb*, has made the point that evolution can be more strongly supported by evidence of telling imperfections than by evidence of perfection. I shall give just two examples.

Fish living on the sea bottom benefit by being flat and hugging the contours. There are two very different kinds of flat fish living on the sea bottom, and they have evolved their flatness in quite different ways. The skates and rays, relatives of sharks, have become flat in what might be called the obvious way. Their bodies have grown out sideways to form great 'wings'. They are like sharks that have passed under a steam roller, but they remain symmetrical and 'the right way up'. Plaice, sole, halibut and their relatives have become flat in a different way. They are bony fish (with swimbladders) related to herrings, trout, etc., and are nothing to do with sharks. Unlike sharks, bony fish as a rule have a marked tendency to be flattened in a vertical direction. A herring, for instance, is much 'taller' than it is wide. It uses its whole, vertically flattened body as a swimming surface, which undulates through the water as it swims. It was natural, therefore, that when the ancestors of plaice and sole took to the sea bottom, they should have lain on one *side* rather than on the belly like the ancestors of skates and rays. But this raised the problem that one eye was always looking down into the sand and was effectively useless. In evolution this problem was solved by the lower eye 'moving' round to the upper side.

We see this process of moving round re-enacted in the development of every young bony flatfish. A young flatfish starts life swimming near the surface, and it is symmetrical and vertically flattened just like a herring. But then the skull starts to grow in a strange, asymmetrical, twisted fashion, so that one eye, for instance the left, moves over the top of the head to finish up on the other side. The young fish settles on the bottom, with both its eyes looking upwards, a strange Picasso-like vision. Incidentally, some species of flatfish settle on the right side, others on the left, and others on either side.

The whole skull of a bony flatfish retains the twisted and distorted evidence of its origins. Its very imperfection is powerful testimony of its ancient history, a history of step-by-step change rather than of deliberate design. No sensible designer would have conceived such a monstrosity if given a free hand to create a flatfish on a clean drawing board. I suspect that most sensible designers would think in terms of something more like a skate. But evolution never starts from a clean drawing board. It has to start from what is already there. In the case of the ancestors of skates this was free-swimming sharks. Sharks in general aren't flattened from side to side as free-swimming bony fish like herrings are. If anything, sharks are already slightly flattened from back to belly. This meant that when some ancient sharks first took to the sea bottom, there was an easy smooth progression to the skate shape, with each intermediate being a slight improvement, given bottom conditions, over its slightly less flattened predecessor.

On the other hand, when the free-swimming ancestor of plaice and halibut, being, like a herring, vertically flattened from side to side, took to the bottom, it was better off lying on its side than balancing precariously on its knife edge of a belly! Even though its evolutionary course was eventually destined to lead it into the complicated and probably costly distortions involved in having two eyes on one side, even though the skate way of being a flat fish might *ultimately* have been the best design for bony fish too, the would-be intermediates that set out along this evolutionary pathway apparently did less well in the short term than their rivals lying on their side. The rivals lying on their side were so much better, in the short term, at hugging the bottom. In evolutionary space, there is a smooth trajectory connecting free-swimming ancestral bony fish to flatfish lying on their side with twisted skulls. There is not a smooth trajectory connecting these bony fish ancestors to flatfish lying on their belly. This speculation cannot be the whole truth, because there are some bony fish that have evolved flatness in a symmetrical, skate-like way. Perhaps their free-swimming ancestors were already slightly flattened for some other reason.

My second example of an evolutionary progression that didn't happen because of disadvantageous intermediates, even though it might ultimately have turned out better if it had, concerns the retina of our eyes (and all other vertebrates). Like any nerve, the optic nerve is a trunk cable, a bundle of separate 'insulated' wires, in this case about three million of them. Each of the three million wires leads from one cell in the retina to the brain. You can think of them as the wires leading from a bank of three million photocells (actually three million relay stations gathering information from an even larger number of photocells) to the computer that is to process the information in the brain. They are gathered together from all over the retina into a single bundle, which is the optic nerve for that eye.

Any engineer would naturally assume that the photocells would point towards the light, with their wires leading backwards towards the brain. He would laugh at any suggestion that the photocells might point away from the light, with their wires departing on the side *nearest* the light. Yet this is exactly what happens in all vertebrate retinas. Each photocell is, in effect, wired in backwards, with its wire sticking out on the side nearest the light. The wire has to travel over the surface of the retina, to a point where it dives through a hole in the retina (the so-called 'blind spot') to join the optic nerve. This means that the light, instead of being granted an unrestricted passage to the photocells, has to pass through a forest of connecting wires, presumably suffering at least some attenuation and distortion (actually probably not much but, still, it is the *principle* of the thing that would offend any tidy-minded engineer!).

I don't know the exact explanation for this strange state of affairs. The relevant period of evolution is so long ago. But I am ready to bet that it had something to do with ancient history and the unserviceable intermediates that would have to be traversed in order to turn the retina the right way round, starting from whatever ancestral organ preceded the eye. Intermediates could see even less well than their imperfect ancestors, and it is no consolation that they are building better eyesight for their remote descendants! What matters is survival in the here and now.

'Dollo's Law' states that evolution is irreversible. This is often confused with a lot of idealistic nonsense about the inevitability of progress, often coupled with ignorant nonsense about evolution 'violating the Second Law of Thermodynamics' (those that belong to the half of the educated population that, according to the novelist C. P. Snow, know what the Second Law is, will realize that it is no more violated by evolution than it is violated by the growth of a baby). There is no reason why general trends in evolution shouldn't be reversed. If there is a trend towards large antlers for a while in evolution, there can easily be a subsequent trend towards smaller antlers again. Dollo's Law is really just a statement about the statistical improbability of following exactly the same evolutionary trajectory twice (or, indeed, any *particular* trajectory), in either direction. A single mutational step can easily be reversed. But for larger numbers of mutational steps the mathematical space of all possible trajectories is so vast that the chance of two trajectories ever arriving at the same point becomes vanishingly small. This is even more true of real animals with their vastly larger numbers of genes. There is nothing mysterious or mystical about Dollo's Law, nor is it something that we go out and 'test' in nature. It follows simply from the elementary laws of probability.

For just the same reason, it is vanishingly improbable that exactly the same evolutionary pathway should ever be travelled twice. And it would seem similarly improbable, for the same statistical reasons, that two lines of evolution should converge on exactly the same endpoint from different starting points.

It is all the more striking a testimony to the power of natural selection, therefore, that numerous examples can be found in real nature, in which independent lines of evolution appear to have converged, from very different starting points, on what looks very like the same endpoint. When we look in detail we find – it would be worrying if we didn't – that the convergence is not total. The different lines of evolution betray their independent origins in numerous points of detail. For instance, octopus eyes are very like ours, but the wires leading from their photocells don't point forwards towards the light, as ours do. Octopus eyes are, in this respect, more 'sensibly' designed. They have arrived at a similar endpoint, from a very different starting point. And the fact is betrayed in details such as this.

Such superficially convergent resemblances are often extremely striking, and I shall devote the rest of the chapter to some of them. They provide most impressive demonstrations of the power of natural selection to put together good designs. Yet the fact that the superficially similar designs also differ, testifies to their independent evolutionary origins and histories. The basic rationale is that, if a design is good enough to evolve once, the same design *principle* is good enough to evolve twice, from different starting points, in different parts of the animal kingdom.

At least two groups of bats, two groups of birds, toothed whales, and probably several other kinds of mammals to a smaller extent, have all independently converged on the technology that humans later redis-covered as sonar! We have no way of knowing whether any other animals now extinct – pterodactyls perhaps? – also evolved the technology independently.

No insects and no fish have so far been found to use sonar, but two quite different groups of fish, one in South America and one in Africa, have developed a somewhat similar navigation system, which appears to be just about as sophisticated and which can be seen as a related, but different, solution to the same problem. These are so-called weakly electric fish. The word 'weakly' is to differentiate them from strongly electric fish, which use electric fields, not to navigate, but to stun their prey. The stunning technique, incid-entally, has also been independently invented by several unrelated groups of fish, for example electric 'eels' (which are not true eels but whose shape is convergent on true eels) and electric rays.

The South American and the African weakly electric fish are quite unrelated to each other, but both live in the same kinds of waters in their respective continents, waters that are too muddy for vision to be effective. The physical principle that they exploit – electric fields in water – is even more alien to our consciousness than the sonar of bats and dolphins. We at least have a subjective idea of what an echo is, but we have almost no subjective idea of what it might be like to perceive an electric field. We didn't even know of the existence of electricity until a couple of centuries ago. We cannot as subjective human beings emphathize with electric fish, but we can, as physicists, understand them.

It is easy to see on the dinner plate that the muscles down each side of any fish are arranged as a row of segments, a *battery* of muscle units. In most fish they contract successively to throw the body into sinuous waves, which propel it forwards. In electric fish, both strongly and weakly electric ones, they have become a battery in the electric sense. Each segment ('cell') of the battery generates a voltage. These voltages are connected up in series along the length of the fish so that, in a strongly electric fish such as an electric eel, the whole battery generates as much as 1 amp at 650 volts. An electric eel is powerful enough to knock a man out. Weakly electric fish don't need high voltages or currents for their purposes, which are purely information-gathering ones.

The principle of electrolocation, as it has been called, is fairly well understood at the level of physics though not, of course, at the level of what it feels like to be an electric fish. The following account applies equally to African and South American weakly electric fish: the convergence is that thorough. Current flows from the front half of the fish, out into the water in lines that curve back and return to the tail end of the fish. There are not really discrete 'lines' but a continuous 'field', an invisible cocoon of electricity surrounding the fish's body. However, for human visualization it is easiest to think in terms of a family of curved lines leaving the fish through a series of portholes spaced along the front half of the body, all curving round in the water and diving into the fish again at the tip of its tail. The fish has what amounts to a tiny voltmeter monitoring the voltage at each 'porthole'. If the fish is suspended in open water with no obstacles around, the lines are smooth curves. The tiny voltmeters at each porthole all register the voltage as 'normal' for their porthole. But if some obstacle appears in the vicinity, say a rock or an item of food, the lines of current that happen to hit the obstacle will be changed. This will change the voltage at any porthole whose current line is affected, and the appropriate voltmeter will register the fact. So in theory a computer, by comparing the pattern of voltages registered by the voltmeters at all the portholes, could calculate the pattern of obstacles around the fish. This is apparently what the fish brain does. This doesn't have to mean that the fish are clever mathematicians. They have an apparatus that solves the necessary equations, just as our brains unconsciously solve equations every time we catch a ball.

It is very important that the fish's own body is kept absolutely rigid. The computer in the head couldn't cope with the extra distortions that would be introduced if the fish's body were bending and twisting like an ordinary fish. Electric fish have, at least twice independently, hit upon this ingenious method of navigation, but they have had to pay a price: they have had to give up the normal, highly efficient, fish method of swimming, throwing the whole body into serpentine waves. They have solved the problem by keeping the body stiff as a poker, but they have a single long fin all the way along the length of the body. Then instead of the whole body being thrown into waves, just the long fin is. The fish's progress through the water is rather slow, but it does move, and apparently the sacrifice of fast movement is worth it: the gains in navigation seem to outweigh the losses in speed of swimming. Fascinatingly, the South American electric fish have hit upon almost exactly the same solution as the African ones, but not quite. The difference is revealing. Both groups have developed a single long fin that runs the whole length of the body, but in the African fish it runs along the back whereas in the South American fish it runs along the belly. This kind of difference in detail is very characteristic of convergent evolution, as we have seen. It is characteristic of convergent designs by human engineers too, of course.

Although the majority of weakly electric fish, in both the African and the South American groups, give their electric discharges in discrete pulses and are called 'pulse' species, a minority of species in both groups do it a different way and are called 'wave' species. I shall not discuss the difference further. What

is interesting is that the pulse/wave split has evolved

twice, independently, in the unrelated New World and Old World groups.

One of the most bizarre examples of convergent evolution that I know concerns the so-called periodical cicadas. Before getting to the convergence, I must fill in some background information. Many insects have a rather rigid separation between a juvenile feeding stage, in which they spend most of their lives, and a relatively brief adult reproducing stage. Mayflies, for instance, spend most of their lives as underwater feeding larvae, then emerge into the air for a single day into which they cram the whole of their adult lives. We can think of the adult as analogous to the ephemeral winged seed of a plant like a sycamore, and the larva as analogous to the main plant, the difference being that sycamores make many seeds and shed them over many successive years, while a mayfly larva gives rise to only one adult right at the end of its own life. Anyway, periodical cicadas have carried the mayfly trend to an extreme. The adults live for a few weeks, but the 'juvenile' stage (technically 'nymphs' rather than larvae) lasts for 13 years (in some varieties) or 17 years (in other varieties). The adults emerge at almost exactly the same moment, having spent 13 (or 17) years cloistered underground. Cicada plagues, which occur in any given area exactly 13 (or 17) years apart, are spectacular eruptions that had led to their incorrectly being called 'locusts' in vernacular American speech. The varieties are known, respectively, as 13-year cicadas and 17-year cicadas.

Now here is the really remarkable fact. It turns out that there is not just one 13-year cicada species and one 17-year species. Rather, there are three species, and each one of the three has both a 17-year and a 13-year variety or race. The division into a 13-year race and a 17-year race has been arrived at independently, no fewer than three times. It looks as though the intermediate periods of 14, 15 and 16 years have been shunned convergently, no fewer than three times. Why? We don't know. The only suggestion anyone has come up with is that what is special about 13 and 17, as opposed to 14, 15 and 16, is that they are prime numbers. A prime number is a number that is not exactly divisible by any other number. The idea is that a race of animals that regularly erupts in plagues gains the benefit of alternately 'swamping' and starving its enemies, predators or parasites. And if these plagues are carefully timed to occur a prime number of years apart, it makes it that much more difficult for the enemies to synchronize their own life cycles. If the cicadas erupted every 14 years, for instance, they could be exploited by a parasite species with a 7-year life cycle. This is a bizarre idea, but no more bizarre than the phenomenon itself. We really don't know what is special about 13 and 17 years. What matters for our purposes here is that there must be *something* special about those numbers, because three different species of cicada have independently converged upon them.

Examples of convergence on a large scale occur when two or more continents are isolated from one another for a long time, and a parallel range of 'trades' is adopted by unrelated animals on each of the continents. By 'trades' I mean ways of making a living, such as burrowing for worms, digging for ants, chasing large herbivores, eating leaves up trees. A good example is the convergent evolution of a whole range of mammal trades in the separate continents of South America, Australia, and the Old World.

These continents weren't always separate. Because our lives are measured in decades, and even our civilizations and dynasties are measured only in centuries, we are accustomed to thinking of the map of the world, the outlines of the continents, as fixed. The theory that continents drifted about was proposed long ago by the German geophysicist Alfred Wegener, but most people laughed at him until well after the Second World War. The admitted fact that South America and Africa look a bit like separated pieces of a jigsaw puzzle was assumed to be just an amusing coincidence. In one of the most rapid and complete revolutions science has known, the formerly controversial theory of 'continental drift' has now become universally accepted under the name of plate tectonics. The evidence that the continents have drifted, that South America did indeed break away from Africa for instance, is now literally overwhelming, but this is not a book about geology and I shall not spell it out. For us the important point is that the timescale on which continents have drifted about is the same slow timescale on which animal lineages have evolved, and we cannot ignore continental drift if we are to understand the patterns of animal evolution on those continents.

Up until about 100 million years ago, then, South America was joined to Africa in the east and to Antarctica in the south. Antarctica was joined to Australia, and India was joined to Africa via Madagascar. There was in fact one huge southern continent, which we now call Gondwanaland, consisting of what is now South America, Africa, Madagascar, India, Antarctica and Australia all rolled into one. There was also a single large northern continent called Laurasia consisting of what is now North America, Greenland, Europe and Asia (apart from India). North America was not connected to South America. About 100 million years ago there was a big break-up of the land masses, and the continents have been slowly moving towards their present positions ever since (they will, of course, continue to move in the future). Africa joined up with Asia via Arabia and became part of the huge continent that we now speak of as the Old World. North America drifted away from Europe, Antarctica drifted south to its present icy location. India detached itself from Africa and set off across what is now called the Indian Ocean, eventually to crunch into south Asia and raise the Himalayas. Australia drifted away from Antarctica into the open sea to become an island continent miles from anywhere else.

It happens that the break-up of the great southern continent of Gondwanaland began during the age of the dinosaurs. When South America and Australia broke away to begin their long periods of isolation from the rest of the world, they each carried their own cargo of dinosaurs, and also of the less-prominent animals that were to become the ancestors of modern 73 mammals. When, rather later, for reasons that are not understood and are the subject of much profitable speculation, the dinosaurs (with the exception of the group of dinosaurs that we now call birds) went extinct, they went extinct all over the world. This left a vacuum in the 'trades' open to land-dwelling animals. The vacuum was filled, over a period of millions of years of evolution, mostly by mammals. The interesting point for us here is that there were three independent vacuums, and they were independently filled by mammals in Australia, South America and the Old World.

The primitive mammals that happened to be around in the three areas when the dinosaurs more or less simultaneously vacated the great life trades, were all rather small and insignificant, probably nocturnal, previously overshadowed and overpowered by the dinosaurs. They could have evolved in radically different directions in the three areas. To some extent this is what happened. There is nothing in the Old World that resembles the giant ground sloth of South America, alas now extinct. The great range of South American mammals included an extinct giant guinea-pig, the size of a modern rhinoceros but a rodent (I have to say 'modern' rhinoceros because the Old

World fauna included a giant rhinoceros the size of a two-storey house). But although the separate continents each produced their unique mammals, the general pattern of evolution in all three areas was the same. In all three areas the mammals that happened to be around at the start fanned out in evolution, and produced a specialist for each trade which, in many cases, came to bear a remarkable resemblance to the corresponding specialist in the other two areas. Each trade, the burrowing trade, the large hunter trade, the plains-grazing trade, and so on, was the subject of independent convergent evolution in two or three separate continents. In addition to these three major sites of independent evolution, smaller islands such as Madagascar have interesting parallel stories of their own, which I shall not go into.

Setting aside the strange egg-laying mammals of Australia – the duck-billed platypus and the spiny anteaters – modern mammals all belong to one of two great groups. These two are the marsupials (whose young are born very small and are then kept in a pouch) and the placentals (all the rest of us). The marsupials came to dominate the Australian story and the placentals the Old World, while the two groups played important roles alongside each other in South

America. The South American story is complicated by the fact that it was subject to sporadic waves of invasion by mammals from North America.

Having set the scene, we can now look at some of the trades and convergences themselves. An important trade is concerned with the exploitation of the great grasslands variously known as prairie, pampas, savannah, etc. Practitioners of this trade include horses (of which the main African species are called zebras and the desert models are called donkeys), and cattle, such as the North American bison, now hunted to near-extinction. Herbivores typically have very long guts containing various kinds of fermenting bacteria, since grass is a poor quality food and needs a lot of digesting. Rather than break their eating up into discrete meals, they typically eat more or less continuously. Huge volumes of plant material flow through them like a river, all the day long. The animals are often very large, and they frequently go about in great herds. Each one of these big herbivores is a mountain of valuable food to any predator that can exploit it. As a consequence of this there is, as we shall see, a whole trade devoted to the difficult task of catching and killing them. These are the predators. Actually, when I say 'a' trade, I really mean a whole lot of 'sub-trades':

lions, leopards, cheetahs, wild dogs and hyenas all hunt in their own specialized ways. The same kind of subdivision is found in the herbivores, and in all the other 'trades'.

The herbivores have keen senses with which they are continuously alert for predators, and they are usually capable of running very fast to escape them. To this end they often have long, spindly legs, and they typically run on the tips of their toes, which have become specially elongated and strengthened in evolution. The nails at the ends of these specialized toes have become large and hard, and we call them hooves. Cattle have two enlarged toes at the extremities of each leg: the familiar 'cloven' hooves. Horses do much the same thing except that, probably for reasons of historical accident, they run on only one toe instead of two. It is derived from what was originally the middle one of the five toes. The other toes have almost completely disappeared over evolutionary time, although they occasionally reappear in freakish 'throwbacks'.

Now South America, as we have seen, was isolated during the period in which horses and cattle were evolving in other parts of the world. But South America has its own great grasslands, and it evolved its own separate groups of large herbivores to exploit the resource. There were massive rhino-like Leviathans that had no connection with true rhinos. The skulls of some of the early South American herbivores suggest that they 'invented' the trunk independently of the true elephants. Some resembled camels, some looked like nothing on earth (today), or like weird chimeras of modern animals. The group called the litopterns are almost unbelievably similar to horses in their legs, yet they were utterly unrelated to horses. The superficial resemblance fooled a nineteenth-century Argentinian expert who thought, with pardonable national pride, that they were the ancestors of all horses in the rest of the world. In fact their resemblance to horses was superficial, and convergent. Grassland life is much the same the world over, and horses and litopterns independently evolved the same qualities to cope with the problems of grassland life. In particular, the litopterns, like the horses, lost all their toes except the middle one on each leg, which became enlarged as the bottom joint of the leg and developed a hoof. The leg of a litoptern is all but indistinguishable from the leg of a horse, yet the two animals are only distantly related.

In Australia the large grazers and browsers are very
different – kangaroos. Kangaroos have the same need

to move rapidly, but they have done it in a different way. Instead of developing four-legged galloping to the high pitch of perfection that horses (and presumably litopterns) did, kangaroos have perfected a different gait: two-legged hopping with a large balancing tail. There is little point in arguing over which of these two gaits is 'better'. They are each highly effective if the body evolves in such a way as to exploit them to the full. Horses and litopterns happened to exploit four-legged galloping, and so ended up with almost identical legs. Kangaroos happened to exploit two-legged hopping, and so ended up with their own uniquely (at least since the dinosaurs) massive hind legs and tail. Kangaroos and horses arrived at different endpoints in 'animal space', probably because of some accidental difference in their starting points.

Turning now to the meat-eaters that the great grazers were running away from, we find some more fascinating convergences. In the Old World we are familiar with such large hunters as wolves, dogs, hyenas, and the big cats – lions, tigers, leopards and cheetahs. A big cat that has only recently gone extinct is the sabretooth ('tiger'), named after its colossal canine teeth which jutted down from the upper jaw in the front of what must have been a terrifying gape. Until recent times there were no true cats or dogs in Australia or the New World (pumas and jaguars are recently evolved from Old World cats). But in both those continents there were marsupial equivalents. In Australia the thylacine, or marsupial 'wolf' (often called the Tasmanian wolf because it survived in Tasmania for a little longer than in mainland Australia), was tragically driven extinct within living memory, slaughtered in enormous numbers as a 'pest' and for 'sport' by humans (there is a slight hope that it may still survive in remote parts of Tasmania, areas which themselves are now threatened with destruction in the interests of providing 'employment' for humans). It is not to be confused with the dingo, by the way, which is a true dog, introduced to Australia more recently by (aboriginal) man. A ciné film made in the 1930s of the last known thylacine, restlessly pacing its lonely zoo cage, shows an uncannily dog like animal, its marsupial nature betrayed only by its slightly undog-like way of holding its pelvis and back legs, presumably something to do with accommodating its pouch. To any dog-lover, the contemplation of this alternative approach to the dog design, this evolutionary traveller along a parallel road separated by 100 million years, this part-familiar yet part utterly alien other-worldly dog, is a moving experience. Maybe they were pests to humans, but humans were much bigger pests to them; now there are no thylacines left and a considerable surplus of humans.

In South America, too, there were no true dogs or cats during the long period of isolation that we are discussing but, as in Australia, there were marsupial equivalents. Probably the most spectacular was *Thylacosmilus*, which looked exactly like the recently extinct sabre-tooth 'tiger' of the Old World, only more so if you see what I mean. Its daggered gape was even wider, and I imagine that it was even more terrifying. Its name records its superficial affinity with the sabre-tooth (*Smilodon*) and the Tasmanian wolf (*Thylacinus*), but in terms of ancestry it is very remote from both. It is slightly closer to the thylacine since both are marsupials, but the two have evolved their big carnivore design independently on different continents; independently of each other and of the placental carnivores, the true cats and dogs of the Old World.

Australia, South America and the Old World offer numerous further examples of multiple convergent evolution. Australia has a marsupial 'mole', superficially almost indistinguishable from the familiar moles of other continents, but pouched, making its living in the same way as other moles and with the same enormously strengthened forepaws for digging. There is a pouched mouse in Australia, though in this case the resemblance is not so close and it does not make its living in quite the same way. Anteating (where 'ants' are deemed for convenience to include termites – another convergence as we shall see) is a 'trade' that is filled by a variety of convergent mammals. They may be subdivided into anteaters that burrow, ant-eaters that climb trees and anteaters that wander over the ground. In Australia, as we might expect, there is a marsupial anteater. Called *Myrmecobius*, it has a long thin snout for poking into ants' nests, and a long sticky tongue with which it mops up its prey. It is a ground-dwelling anteater. Australia also has a burrowing ant-eater, the spiny anteater. This is not a marsupial, but a member of the group of egg-laying mammals, the monotremes, so remote from us that marsupials are our close cousins by comparison. The spiny anteater, too, has a long pointed snout, but its spines give it a superficial resemblance to a hedgehog rather than to another typical anteater.

South America could easily have had a marsupial anteater, alongside its marsupial sabre-tooth 'tiger', but as it happens the anteater trade was early filled by placental mammals instead. The largest of today's anteaters is *Myrmecophaga* (which just means anteater in Greek), the large ground-wandering anteater of South America and probably the most extreme anteating specialist in the world. Like the Australian marsupial *Myrmecobius*, it has a long and pointed snout, extremely long and pointed in this case, and an extremely long sticky tongue. South America also has a small tree-climbing anteater, which is a close cousin of *Myrmecophaga* and looks like a miniature and less extreme version of it, and a third, intermediate form. Although placental mammals, these anteaters are very far from any Old World placentals. They belong to a uniquely South American family, which also includes armadillos and sloths. This ancient placental family coexisted with the marsupials from the early days of the continent's isolation.

The Old World anteaters include various species of pangolin in Africa and Asia, ranging from tree-climbing forms to digging forms, all looking a bit like fircones with pointed snouts. Also in Africa is the weird ant-bear or aardvark, which is partially specialized for digging. A feature that characterizes all anteaters, whether marsupial, monotreme or placental, is an extremely low metabolic rate. The metabolic rate is the rate at which their chemical 'fires' burn, most easily measured as the blood temperature. There is a tendency for metabolic rate to depend on body size in mammals generally. Smaller animals tend to have higher metabolic rates, just as the engines of small cars tend to turn over at a higher rate than those of larger cars. But some animals have high metabolic rates for their size, and anteaters, of whatever ancestry and affinities, tend to have very low metabolic rates for their size. It is not obvious why this is, but it is so strikingly convergent among animals that have nothing else in common but their anteating habit, that it almost certainly is somehow related to this habit.

As we have seen, the 'ants' that anteaters eat are often not true ants at all, but termites. Termites are often known as 'white ants', but they are related to cockroaches, rather than to true ants, which are related to bees and wasps. Termites resemble ants superficially because they have convergently adopted the same habits. The same range of habits, I should say, because there are many different branches of the ant/termite trade, and both ants and termites have independently adopted most of them. As so often with convergent evolution, the differences are revealing as well as the similarities.

Both ants and termites live in large colonies consisting mostly of sterile, wingless workers, dedicated to the efficient production of winged reproductive castes which fly off to found new colonies. An interesting difference is that in ants the workers are all sterile females, whereas in termites they are sterile males and sterile females. Both ant and termite colonies have one (or sometimes several) enlarged 'queens', sometimes (in both ants and termites) grotesquely enlarged. In both ants and termites the workers can include specialist castes such as soldiers. Sometimes these are such dedicated fighting machines, especially in their huge jaws (in the case of ants, but 'gun-turrets' for chemical warfare in the case of termites), that they are incapable of feeding themselves and have to be fed by non-soldier workers. Particular species of ants parallel particular species of termites. For example, the habit of fungus-farming has arisen independently in ants (in the New World) and termites (in Africa). The ants (or termites) forage for plant material that they do not digest themselves but make into compost on which they grow fungi. It is the fungi that they themselves eat. The fungi, in both cases, grow nowhere else than in the nests of ants or termites, respectively. The fungus-farming habit has also been discovered independently 85 and convergently (more than once) by several species of beetles.

There are also interesting convergences within the ants. Although most ant colonies live a settled existence in a fixed nest, there seems to be a successful living to be made by wandering in enormous pillaging armies. This is called the legionary habit. Obviously all ants walk about and forage, but most kinds return to a fixed nest with their booty, and the queen and the brood are left behind in the nest. The key to the wandering legionary habit, on the other hand, is that the armies take the brood and the queen with them. The eggs and larvae are carried in the jaws of workers. In Africa the legionary habit has been developed by the so-called driver ants. In Central and South America the parallel 'army ants' are very similar to driver ants in habit and appearance. They are not particularly closely related. They have certainly evolved the characteristics of the 'army' trade independently and convergently.

Both driver ants and army ants have exceptionally large colonies, up to a million in army ants, up to about 20 million in driver ants. Both have nomadic phases alternating with 'statary' phases, relatively stable encampments or 'bivouacs'. Army ants and driver ants, or rather their colonies taken together as amoeba-like units, are both ruthless and terrible predators of their respective jungles. Both cut to pieces anything animal in their path, and both have acquired a mystique of terror in their own land. Villagers in parts of South America are reputed traditionally to vacate their villages, lock, stock and barrel, when a large ant army is approaching, and to return when the legions have marched through, having cleaned out every cockroach, spider and scorpion even from the thatched roofs. I remember as a child in Africa being more frightened of driver ants than of lions or crocodiles. It is worth getting this formidable reputation into perspective by quoting the words of Edward O. Wilson, the world's foremost authority on ants as well as the author of *Sociobiology*:

In answer to the single question I am asked most frequently about ants, I can give the following answer: No, driver ants are not really the terror of the jungle. Although the driver ant colony is an 'animal' weighing in excess of 20 kg and possessing on the order of 20 million mouths and stings and is surely the most formidable creation of the insect world, it still does not match up to the lurid stories told about it. After all, the swarm can only cover about a metre of ground every three minutes. Any competent bush mouse, not to mention man or elephant, can step aside and contemplate the whole grass-roots frenzy at leisure, an object less of menace than of strangeness and wonder, the culmination of an evolutionary story as different from that of mammals as it is possible to conceive in this world.

As an adult in Panama I have stepped aside and contemplated the New World equivalent of the driver ants that I had feared as a child in Africa, flowing by me like a crackling river, and I can testify to the strangeness and wonder. Hour after hour the legions marched past, walking as much over each others' bodies as over the ground, while I waited for the queen. Finally she came, and hers was a wonderful strange presence. It was impossible to see her body. She appeared only as a moving wave of worker frenzy, a boiling peristaltic ball of ants with linked arms. She was somewhere in the middle of the seething ball of workers, while all around it the massed ranks of soldiers faced threateningly outwards with jaws agape, every one prepared to kill and to die in defence of the queen. Forgive my curiosity to see her: I prodded the ball of workers with a long stick, in a vain attempt to flush out the queen. Instantly 20 soldiers buried their massively muscled pincers in my stick, possibly never to let go, while dozens more swarmed up the stick causing me to let go with alacrity.

I never did glimpse the queen, but somewhere inside that boiling ball she was, the central data bank, the repository of the master DNA of the whole colony. Those gaping soldiers were prepared to die for the queen, not because they loved their mother, not because they had been drilled in the ideals of patriotism, but simply because their brains and their jaws were built by genes stamped from the master die carried in the queen herself. They behaved like brave soldiers because they had inherited the genes of a long line of ancestral queens whose lives, and whose genes, had been saved by soldiers as brave as themselves. My soldiers had inherited the same genes from the present queen as those old soldiers had inherited from the ancestral queens. My soldiers were guarding the master copies of the very instructions that made them to the guarding. They were guarding the wisdom of their ancestors, the Ark of the Covenant.

I felt the strangeness then, and the wonder, not unmixed with revivals of half-forgotten fears, but transfigured and enhanced by a mature understanding, which I had lacked as a child in Africa, of what the whole performance was for. Enhanced, too, by the 89 knowledge that this story of the legions had reached the same evolutionary culmination not once but twice. These were not the driver ants of my childhood nightmares, however similar they might be, but remote, New World cousins. They were doing the same thing as the driver ants, and for the same reasons. It was night now and I turned for home, an awestruck child again, but joyful in the new world of understanding that had supplanted the dark, African fears.

READ MORE IN PENGUIN

For complete information about books available from Penguin and how to order them, please write to us at the appropriate address below. Please note that for copyright reasons the selection of books varies from country to country.

IN THE UNITED KINGDOM: Please write to *Dept. EP, Penguin Books Ltd, Bath Road, Harmondsworth, Middlesex UB7 0DA.*

IN THE UNITED STATES: Please write to *Consumer Sales, Penguin USA, P.O. Box 999, Dept. 17109, Bergenfield, New Jersey 07621-0120.* VISA and MasterCard holders call 1-800-253-6476 to order Penguin titles.

IN CANADA: Please write to *Penguin Books Canada Ltd, 10 Alcorn Avenue, Suite 300, Toronto, Ontario M4V 3B2.*

IN AUSTRALIA: Please write to *Penguin Books Australia Ltd, P.O. Box 257, Ringwood, Victoria 3134.*

IN NEW ZEALAND: Please write to *Penguin Books (NZ) Ltd, Private Bag 102902, North Shore Mail Centre, Auckland 10.*

IN INDIA: Please write to *Penguin Books India Pvt Ltd, 706 Eros Apartments, 56 Nehru Place, New Delhi 110 019.*

IN THE NETHERLANDS: Please write to *Penguin Books Netherlands bv, Postbus 3507, NL-1001 AH Amsterdam.*

IN GERMANY: Please write to *Penguin Books Deutschland GmbH, Metzlerstrasse 26, 60594 Frankfurt am Main.*

IN SPAIN: Please write to *Penguin Books S. A., Bravo Murillo 19, 1° B, 28015 Madrid.*

IN ITALY: Please write to *Penguin Italia s.r.l., Via Felice Casati 20, I-20124 Milano.*

IN FRANCE: Please write to *Penguin France S. A., 17 rue Lejeune, F-31000 Toulouse.*

IN JAPAN: Please write to *Penguin Books Japan, Ishikiribashi Building, 2-5-4, Suido, Bunkyo-ku, Tokyo 112.*

IN GREECE: Please write to *Penguin Hellas Ltd, Dimocritou 3, GR-106 71 Athens.*

IN SOUTH AFRICA: Please write to *Longman Penguin Southern Africa (Pty) Ltd, Private Bag X08, Bertsham 2013.*